Weekly Reader
Children's Book Club
presents

ME!

ME!

A First Book of Poems for Children
compiled by
Lee Bennett Hopkins
illustrated by
Tālivaldis Stubis

Houghton Mifflin/Clarion Books/New York

For my brother, Donald, who grew up with me. L.B.H.

ACKNOWLEDGMENTS

Thanks are due to the following authors and publishers for permission to use the material included:

Atheneum Publishers for "Tree Climbing" from *Stilts, Somersaults, and Headstands* by Kathleen Fraser. Copyright © 1968 by Kathleen Fraser.

Follett Publishing Company for "Hamsters" from *That Was Summer* by Marci Ridlon. Copyright © 1969 by Marci Ridlon. Used by permission of Follett Publishing Company.

Harcourt, Brace & World, Inc. for "Bump on my Knee" from *Wide Awake and Other Poems* by Myra Cohn Livingston. Copyright © 1959 by Myra Cohn Livingston. Reprinted by permission of Harcourt, Brace & World, Inc.

Harper & Row, Publishers for "Robert, Who Is Often a Stranger to Himself" and "Skipper" from *Bronzeville Boys and Girls* by Gwendolyn Brooks. Copyright © 1956 by Gwendolyn Brooks Blakely. "Look" and "Nobody Loves Me" from *All That Sunlight* by Charlotte Zolotow. Copyright © 1967 by Charlotte Zolotow. All reprinted with permission of Harper & Row, Publishers.

Holt, Rinehart & Winston, Inc. for "An Indignant Male" from *Five Going on Six* by A. B. Ross. All rights reserved. Reprinted by permission of Holt, Rinehart & Winston, Inc.

Lee Bennett Hopkins for "This Tooth" and "Toy Telephone." Copyright © 1970 by Lee Bennett Hopkins.

Houghton Mifflin Company for "Christmas Eve Rhyme" from *Sweet As A Pickle and Clean As A Pig* by Carson McCullers. Copyright © 1964 by Carson McCullers. Reprinted by permission of Houghton Mifflin Company.

Larry Kirkman for "An Itch." Copyright © 1970 by Larry Kirkman.

Little, Brown and Company for "A Year Later" from *Hello and Good-by* by Mary Ann and Norman Hoberman. Copyright © 1959 by Mary Ann and Norman Hoberman. Reprinted by permission of Little, Brown and Company.

G. P. Putnam's Sons for "Everybody Says" from *Here, There and Everywhere* by Dorothy Aldis. Copyright 1927, 1928 by Dorothy Aldis. "My Nose" from *All Together* by Dorothy Aldis. Copyright 1925, 1926, 1927, 1928, 1934, 1939, 1952 by Dorothy Aldis. Reprinted by permission of G. P. Putnam's Sons.

Scott, Foresman and Company for "After a Bath" from *Up the Windy Hill* by Aileen Fisher. Reprinted by permission of Scott, Foresman and Company.

Simon & Schuster, Inc. for "Mirror, Mirror" from *Miracles*, compiled by Richard Lewis. Copyright © 1966 by Richard Lewis. Reprinted by permission of Simon & Schuster, Inc.

This book is a presentation of
Weekly Reader Children's Book Club.

Weekly Reader Children's Book Club
offers book clubs for children from
preschool through junior high school.
All quality hardcover books are selected by
a distinguished Weekly Reader Selection Board.

For further information write to:
Weekly Reader Children's Book Club
1250 Fairwood Ave.
Columbus, Ohio 43216

CONTENTS

ROBERT, WHO IS OFTEN
A STRANGER TO HIMSELF

Do you ever look in the looking-glass
And see a stranger there?
A child you know and do not know,
Wearing what you wear?

GWENDOLYN BROOKS

MIRROR! MIRROR!

As I look into the mirror I see my face.
Then I talk to myself.
Then I play like I am in jail.
I pretend that I am bad.
I pretend sometimes that I am on a stage.
I sing to myself.   I introduce people.

DEBORAH ENSIGN

LOOK

Firelight and shadows
dancing on the wall.
Look at my shadow
    TEN FEET TALL!

CHARLOTTE ZOLOTOW

HERE AM I

Here am I,
Little Jumping Joan;
When nobody's with me,
I'm all alone.

MOTHER GOOSE

TREE CLIMBING

This is my tree,
my place to be alone in,
my branches for climbing,
my green leaves for hiding in,
my sunshine for reading,
my clouds for dreaming,
my sky for singing,
my tree, my beautiful tree.

KATHLEEN FRASER

AN INDIGNANT MALE

The way they scrub
Me in the tub,
I think there's
    Hardly
    Any
    Doubt
Sometime they'll rub
And rub and rub
Until they simply
    Rub
    Me
    Out.

A. B. ROSS

AFTER A BATH

After my bath
I try, try, try
to wipe myself
till I'm dry, dry, dry.

Hands to wipe
and fingers and toes
and two wet legs
and a shiny nose.

Just think how much
less time I'd take
if I were a dog
and could shake, shake, shake.

AILEEN FISHER

13

MY NOSE

It doesn't breathe,
It doesn't smell,
It doesn't feel
So very well.

I am discouraged
With my nose.
The only thing it
Does is blows.

DOROTHY ALDIS

THIS TOOTH

I jiggled it
    jaggled it
    jerked it.

I pushed
    and pulled
    and poked it.

But—

As soon as I stopped, and left it alone,
This tooth came out on its very own!

LEE BENNETT HOPKINS

EVERYBODY SAYS

Everybody says
I look just like my mother.
Everybody says
I'm the image of Aunt Bee.
Everybody says
My nose is like my father's
But *I* want to look like ME!

DOROTHY ALDIS

SKIPPER

I looked in the fish-glass,
And what did I see.
A pale little gold fish
Looked sadly at me.
At the base of the bowl,
So still, he was lying.
"Are you dead, little fish?"
"Oh, no! But I'm dying."
I gave him fresh water
And the best of fish food—
But it was too late.
I did him no good.
I buried him by
Our old garden tree.
Our old garden tree
Will protect him for me.

GWENDOLYN BROOKS

HAMSTERS

Hamsters are the nicest things
That anyone could own.
I like them even better than
Some dogs that I have known.

Their fur is soft, their faces nice.
They're small when they are grown.
And they sit inside your pocket
When you are all alone.

MARCI RIDLON

TOY TELEPHONE
(for J.G.)

When nobody's around to play with me
And I am all alone,
The thing I like the most to do
Is use my telephone.

I can talk to Grandma,
The astronauts, a ghost!
I can talk to anyone
I want to talk to most.

I talk and talk and talk and talk
Until I look to see,
My friend outside the window
Who'll *really* talk to me.

LEE BENNETT HOPKINS

NOBODY LOVES ME

Somedays,
nobody loves me
so I go down the names
I know:
      I hate Martha
      I hate James
      I hate Selma
      I hate Jo.
Nobody likes me,
that I know.

Somedays,
everyone loves me
so I go down the names
I know:
      I love Martha
      I love James
      I love Selma
      I love Jo.
Everyone loves me,
I know so!

CHARLOTTE ZOLOTOW

BUMP ON MY KNEE

Look at the terrible bump
        on my knee
(I thought I was playing carefully,
        but the wheel turned round
        and I suddenly found
        myself on the ground)
It doesn't hurt terribly
        but I think
        I would like
        you to paint it
        a
        beautiful
        pink!

MYRA COHN LIVINGSTON

AN ITCH

One day
    I itched
        On my back

           I couldn't reach it
           I couldn't itch it

           But my friend
               loved to scratch

And he wrote his name
On my back
With his fingernails.

LARRY KIRKMAN

CHRISTMAS EVE RHYME

My best friend is Jimmy
He has no chimney.
So what will happen at Christmas time?
When Santa flies over the houses
And stops at each chimney
Will he skip Jimmy
Who has no chimney?

CARSON MCCULLERS

A YEAR LATER

Last summer I couldn't swim at all;
I couldn't even float!
I had to use a rubber tube
Or hang on to a boat;
I had to sit on shore
While everybody swam.
But now it's this summer
And I can!

MARY ANN HOBERMAN